THE QUIZ BOOK FOR SPIES

by H. Becker

Scholastic Canada Ltd.
Toronto New York London Auckland Sydney
Mexico City New Delhi Hong Kong Buenos Aires

Scholastic Canada Ltd.
604 King Street West, Toronto, Ontario M5V 1E1, Canada

Scholastic Inc.
557 Broadway, New York, NY 10012, USA

Scholastic Australia Pty Limited
PO Box 579, Gosford, NSW 2250, Australia

Scholastic New Zealand Limited
Private Bag 94407, Botany, Manukau 2163, New Zealand

Scholastic Children's Books
Euston House, 24 Eversholt Street, London NW1 1DB, UK

www.scholastic.ca

ISBN 978-1-4431-1338-0

6 5 4 3 2   Printed in Canada 121   15 16 17 18 19

MIX
Paper from
responsible sources
FSC® C004071

Table of Contents

DO YOU HAVE
WHAT IT TAKES?

Are you spy material or just a Nosy Parker? Answer yes or no to each of the following questions.

1. I follow directions well.
2. I consider myself to be average-looking — not great, not hideous.
3. I tend to be independent — neither a leader, nor a follower.
4. I'm usually the life of the party.
5. I possess a cherished collection of something I wouldn't want others to know about — like shrunken lizard heads or a zillion Beanie Babies.
6. I speak more than one language.
7. I am the smartest kid in my class.
8. I have a bad temper.
9. I have a strong sense of duty.
10. I get nervous when I tell a lie.

Scoring

1. Yes 20   No 0
2. Yes 15   No 0
3. Yes 5   No 0
4. Yes 0   No 20
5. Yes 0   No 10
6. Yes 25   No 0
7. Yes 25   No 0
8. Yes 0   No 20
9. Yes 15   No 0
10. Yes 0   No 20

How you rate . . .

0–75 Honest Ed. You cannot tell a lie. The truth is you're too open, too honest and too much fun to do the sneaky work of spying. Consider a career on stage or in politics instead.

80–120 Mr. Ambassador. You love the idea of being a spy, but might find the demands of the job don't really suit your outgoing nature. A job as a high-level diplomat might be the one for you. The party favours at the embassy are excellent.

125–150 Sneaky Pete. You have many talents, but few people notice. Congratulations! That's the perfect skill set for a successful spy. It lets you fly under the radar and outwit and outsmart everyone!

155+ Dastardly Dan. Your score cannot be checked because someone stole the answer key — you! Espionage was invented for people like you: smart, silent and sneaky. Please, please, please decide to work for the good guys, okay?

WHICH FICTIONAL SPY ARE YOU?

Are you a super-cool spy like James Bond, or are you more of a *Spy Kids* sort of agent? Answer yes or no to each of the following questions to find out your inner spy personality.

1. You're a skilled snowboarder.
2. You like dressing in a suit and tie.
3. You care about your hair and have the super-strength gel to prove it.
4. You love to stand out in a crowd.
5. At times, you can be somewhat immature.
6. Actually, you are VERY immature. You can be downright childish.
7. People underestimate you.
8. You like to play it cool — it's hard to guess what you're thinking.
9. You prefer hanging out with friends rather than being "the lone wolf."
10. *Habla español* (you speak Spanish) or another language besides English.
11. You come from a family of sneaky people.
12. You are an optimist who thinks everything is groovy!

Scoring

1. Yes 15 No 0	4. Yes 10 No 20	7. Yes 0 No 20	10. *Si* 10 No 0
2. Yes 20 No 5	5. Yes 5 No 20	8. Yes 25 No 0	11. Yes 10 No 0
3. Yes 15 No 5	6. Yes 5 No 20	9. Yes 5 No 20	12. Yes 0 No 20

CONFIDENTIAL

You are ...

35–60 Austin Powers. You are a little klutzy, but your great sense of humour works in your favour. You are very open and love all things psychedelic. You wish you had a time machine and better teeth.

65–95 Juni Cortez, from *Spy Kids*. You are impatient, but you can sit in front of the TV for hours. You are very family-oriented. You are smarter than you look.

100–135 Zac Power. You are tough as nails, a clutch player with a love of books and wombats. You're a little vain, but, hey, you have a right to be! Your favourite expression is, "I've got the power!"

140–180 Alex Rider. You are curious, capable and wish you were allowed to drive. You love riding skateboards, horses and unicycles. You want to know what a "lex" is.

185+ James Bond. You are cooler than an ice cube in the Arctic. Dress for success is your motto. You like gadgets, especially if they turn into cars. Your word is your bond.

WHICH FICTIONAL SPY VILLAIN ARE YOU?

If you turned your formidable spy skills toward evil, what kind of criminal mastermind would you be? To find out, answer yes or no to each of the following questions.

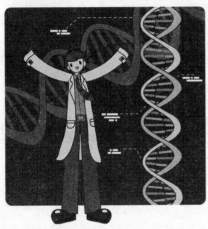

1. You are very talkative.
2. You would like to clone yourself.
3. You are a natural performer.
4. You like the idea of a career in medicine.
5. You'd like to shave your head one day.

6. You consider yourself a video game expert.
7. You would love to have a secret lair on your own island.
8. Your personality can be described as lively or animated.
9. You have sometimes been described as cold. Frozen, actually.
10. You like to draw smiley faces on everything you own.

CONFIDENTIAL

TOP SECRET

Scoring

1. Yes 20	No 5	5. Yes 15	No 0	9. Yes 20	No 0
2. Yes 15	No 0	6. Yes 0	No 20	10. Yes 5	No 0
3. Yes 10	No 0	7. Yes 15	No 0		
4. Yes 15	No 0	8. Yes 10	No 5		

You are . . .

10–15 So Sorry. You are not a super-spy villain, just an ordinary regular villain.

20–40 Mr. Grin, Alex Rider's Enemy. Cat got your tongue? You tend to hold your own counsel and speak only when spoken to. But you can be fierce when crossed. Keep smiling — that will keep everybody guessing!

45–65 Jazz Hands, the Enemy in *Totally Spies.* You are an excellent mime and think actions speak louder than words. You can be very dramatic, in a quiet sort of way. Stay out of invisible boxes.

70–90 The Toymaker, Enemy of the Cortez Family.
You love all things electronic. You enjoy building with construction sets such as Lego and K'NEX. You can be level-headed, but dislike when people play with your stuff. You think lava is cool.

95–115 Dr. No, James Bond's Enemy. You tend to be negative. You are also very stubborn and refuse to take no for an answer. Should you lose your arms, invest in a good pair of replacements — they'll come in handy!

120+ Dr. Evil, Austin Powers' Enemy. You could be a comedian if you weren't so darn scary. You may be evil, but you have a tender spot for, well, miniature versions of yourself! A word of advice? Don't forget to get your moles checked out.

CONFIDENTIAL

CAN YOU COMPLETE
THIS MISSION PERFECTLY?

Spies need to follow instructions to the letter. Take this quiz to see if your skills will spell success in espionage work.

1. Go to the bottom of the page. There is a number written there. What is it?

2. Count out that number of words from the start of the first paragraph on this page. What is the word?

3. Count the number of letters in that word. Count BACKWARDS that number from the word you just identified. What is the word you arrive at?

4. That word is a clue to how many words you will now count forward. Count forward that number. What word do you land on?

5. How many of them are in that word?

6. Get up and do that number of jumping jacks. How many jumping jacks will that be?

7. Did you do the jumping jacks or skip that instruction?

8. Stand up, shout "Vive la France!" three times, then sit down again.

9. Say to a friend, "Do you see that bug under there?" If they reply, "Under where?" say, "Ha! Ha! I made you say underwear!"

10. Close this book now and go write about this quiz in your diary.

10

CONFIDENTIAL

Scoring

Give yourself 1 point for each correct answer.

1. 10
2. this
3. to
4. letter
5. 6
6. 6
7. If you did the jumping jacks, go on to number 8. If you did not do the jumping jacks, you FAIL this quiz. It's on following instructions, after all!
8. If you stood up and shouted "Vive la France!" go on to number 9. If you did not, you FAIL this quiz. Especially if you did the jumping jacks in number 6. What, you like jumping up and down better than France? Doesn't matter. You were supposed to follow all the instructions, even the ones you don't like. Long live France!
9. If you said, "Do you see that bug under there?" to a friend, go on to number 10. If you did not, you FAIL this quiz. It's STILL on following instructions, duh!
10. Did you close the book and write in your diary? If you did, you FAIL this test. No real spy *ever* keeps a diary!

How you rate . . .

0–3 You Are a Leader, Not a Follower. Not a great skill set for a spy. But don't fret — your destiny is to become leader of the free world!

4–6 Yes, Sir, Captain, Sir! You have a future in the military. Watch out for shrapnel.

7–8 Letter Perfect. You know how to follow instructions to the letter. You'll enjoy a successful spell as a spy.

9–10 Instruction Ace. There's nothing left to teach you. You will self-destruct in ten seconds.

WHICH FAMOUS
REAL-LIFE SPY ARE YOU?

Fictional spies may be fun, but real-life spies can be even more amazing than made-up ones. Take this quiz to discover which actual agent your personality most resembles.

1. Your favourite food is . . .
   a. meat pies.
   b. pizza.
   c. chocolate.
   d. chicken Kiev.

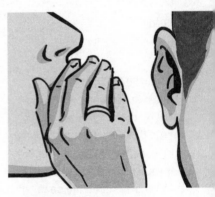

2. How would you describe yourself?
   a. Extremely loyal.
   b. I can be bought.
   c. Loyal, if deserved.
   d. I am loyal only to myself.

3. Are you . . .
   a. outdoorsy: into camping and backpacking?
   b. a city slicker?
   c. an intellectual?
   d. the type that prefers the simple life?

4. Are you good at keeping secrets?
   a. Yes.
   b. Sort of.
   c. No.
   d. Depends whose secrets they are.

5. Which era do you think you'd be happiest living in?
   a. 1960s
   b. 1800s
   c. 1940s
   d. Now

CONFIDENTIAL

Scoring

1. a5 b10 c0 d20
2. a5 b15 c0 d10
3. a5 b10 c15 d0
4. a0 b10 c15 d20
5. a20 b0 c10 d15

You are . . .

0–5 Laura Secord. Laura Secord was a housewife who overheard Americans plotting against the Canadians and British during the War of 1812. The story goes that after she heard the American general making plans for an attack, she walked for 18 hours to report the news to the British military, saving the day.

10–30 Sir William Stephenson. A Canadian spy, he worked for the British during World War II. Codenamed Intrepid, he is widely considered to be one of the real-life spies James Bond was based on.

35–50 Sir Robert Baden-Powell. Founder of the Boy Scouts, Sir Robert Baden-Powell spied for the British during several campaigns, including the Second Boer War. To gain access to off-limits areas, he would sometimes pose as a butterfly collector!

55–65 Giacomo Casanova. His name is synonymous with romance and success with the ladies, but Giacomo Casanova was also an adventurer, gambler, writer and con man who acted as a spy — first for the French, then for the Inquisition in Venice. He ended his life in exile, working as a librarian!

70–80 Robert Hanssen. American Robert Hanssen spied for the Soviet Union from 1979 to 2001. He is considered to be the cause of the worst intelligence disaster in U.S. history. He is now serving a life sentence, with no chance of parole, for 15 counts of espionage.

85+ Kim Philby. A high-ranking officer in the British secret service, Philby really worked as a double agent for the Soviet Union. He is part of the notorious Cambridge Five, a group of intellectuals who were all KGB spies. He defected to the Soviet Union in 1963.

CONFIDENTIAL

ARE YOU CUT OUT TO BE A SPYMASTER?

Spymasters are the top dogs — the spies who run the entire operation. They have different skills than agents in the field. Are you a future spymaster?

1. How would you describe yourself?
   a. Logical.
   b. Laid back.
   c. Can see "the big picture."
   d. Obsessed. Totally obsessed.

2. A friend does something to make you mad. What do you do?
   a. Plot my revenge: underpants on the flag pole.
   b. Stew about it.
   c. Confront them and work it out.
   d. Nothing — things like that don't get to me.

3. You are starting the ropes course in gym. You've never done it before. How do you react?
   a. With excitement. I can't wait to try it!
   b. With fear — it looks scary.
   c. Calmly — I'll handle it, no problem.
   d. Tell a joke: "What did the snake say to the rope?" "What did I do to deserve the silent treatment?"

4. Your friends have all been assigned to a different class next term. You . . .
   a. couldn't care less. You'll find new victims — er, friends . . .
   b. panic — you don't want to be on your own!
   c. feel sad, but know you'll make new friends and still see the old ones at recess.
   d. seethe — how could THEY do this to YOU?

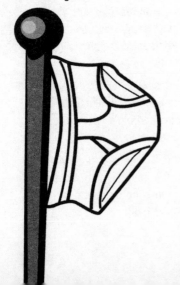

5. You've been assigned to do a group project in class. You . . .
   a. looooove the idea of having minions to do the work for you!
   b. draw up a plan and delegate tasks.
   c. dislike having to rely on others to get a good mark.
   d. can't wait to have fun goofing around with your classmates.

6. Which do you enjoy most?
   a. Playing a team sport.
   b. Doing an individual sport.
   c. Solving a crossword puzzle.
   d. Watching *Phineas and Ferb*.

7. People say you are . . .
   a. a good communicator.
   b. completely off the wall. *Ka-boing! Ka-boing!*
   c. fun to be around.
   d. determined and disciplined.

8. What is your favourite school subject?
   a. Physical education.
   b. Science.
   c. English.
   d. I like them all, but especially lunch and recess.

9. Which do you prefer?
   a. An adrenalin-rush adventure.
   b. A regular routine.
   c. Taking things easy.
   d. To be busy and on the go.

10. You're working on a tricky homework problem and can't seem to solve it. You . . .
    a. consult a fortune-telling chicken to get the answer.
    b. put it aside and ask your teacher about it in the morning.
    c. never say die! Keep working, and working, and working.
    d. do some more research, then finish your homework.

CONFIDENTIAL

Scoring

1. a3 b1 c3 d4
2. a4 b1 c3 d2
3. a2 b0 c3 d1
4. a4 b0 c3 d4
5. a4 b3 c2 d1
6. a3 b2 c3 d0
7. a3 b4 c1 d3
8. a2 b4 c3 d0
9. a4 b2 c1 d3
10. a4 b1 c2 d3

How you rate . . .

6–8 Master Class. Good work on getting dressed this morning. Alas, knowing how to put on your shoes is not all you will need to become a spymaster. Keep trying and reapply when you have mastered tying shoelaces!

9–15 Masterpiece! Not really — your spy skills are more like fingerpainting than fine art. However, that doesn't mean you don't have what it takes to be great at something else just as important, but maybe more suited to your temperament and abilities.

16–22 Mixmaster. Your mix of skills is the envy of every food processor. When you've finished blending smoothies for your staff, you'll make an excellent spymaster/chef.

23–33 Spymaster of the Universe. Awesome! You get to boss around Bond.

34+ Supreme Leader of the Bad Guys. You may not be very smart, or sane, but you make up for it with your unfailing determination to blow up the planet!

CONFIDENTIAL

DO YOU KNOW YOUR SPY SLANG?

Could you be a mole or a sleeper? A cobbler or a babysitter? Get the inside scoop on spy lingo. You don't want to be exposed by your sloppy slang.

1. A babysitter is . . .
   a. a place to hide covert information.
   b. a bodyguard.
   c. a case officer.
   d. Sarah, the teenager who watches me every Tuesday when my parents go curling.

2. What's a mole?
   a. A small furry animal with a birthmark.
   b. A coded message.
   c. A spy who has infiltrated an enemy organization.
   d. A chocolate sauce.

3. A false passport is called . . .
   a. a shoe.
   b. a slipper.
   c. a sneaker.
   d. snizzleswit.

4. What's a dead drop?
   a. An assassin.
   b. An assassin's weapon.
   c. A place to hide covert information.
   d. *Bungeeeeeeeeee!*

5. A spy who creates false documents is called a . . .
   a. cobbler.
   b. candlestick maker.
   c. candyman.
   d. documentary producer.

6. Steganography is . . .
   a. the art of making dinosaurs.
   b. the art of hiding information.
   c. the art of hiding dinosaurs.
   d. a kind of dinosaur.

7. Should you worry if you've been "rolled up"?
   a. No, it means I've been given a new legend.
   b. Yes, I've been captured.
   c. Yes, I've been found in enemy territory.
   d. Yes, because I've been rolled up in a carpet and sold to my enemies!

CONFIDENTIAL

8. A jack-in-the-box is . . .

    a. an enemy spy inside your organization.

    b. a pop-up dummy used so a live agent can escape unseen.

    c. a mission at sea.

    d. a really creepy toy that plays the song "Pop Goes the Weasel."

9. A sleeper is . . .

    a. a dud agent who does a poor job.

    b. an enemy agent's home.

    c. a spy who lives quietly among his/her enemies until called into service.

    d. you, every morning when your dad tries to wake you up for school.

10. What's a legend?

    a. A spy who has saved the world.

    b. A spy who has saved the world. Twice.

    c. A made-up cover story.

    d. A code name.

Scoring

Give yourself 1 point for each right answer.

1. b	3. a	5. a	7. b	9. c
2. c	4. c	6. b	8. b	10. c

How you rate . . .

0–1 Um . . . Please just turn yourself in already and save everyone a lot of work!

2–6 Lord of Lingo! You've been studying.

7–9 Slangtastic! Go to the head of the class.

10 Top Talker! You're a born spy!

CONFIDENTIAL

SPY WORLD

Can you match the spy job descriptions listed here to their sneaky titles?

1. Linguist

2. Surveillance Officer

3. Communications Officer

4. Forensic Expert

5. Tech Officer

6. Sleeper

7. Mole

8. Surreptitious-Entry Specialist

9. Counter-Intelligence Agent

10. Cryptologist

a. enemy agent working inside your operation

b. decodes and analyzes secret messages

c. creates and spreads false information to confuse the enemy

d. inactive agent waiting for assignment at a later date

e. creates and manages gadgets, such as surveillance devices, cameras and satellite technology

f. oversees staff that gathers and analyzes information

g. observes targets in the field

h. collects information by gaining entry to field locations without being detected

i. responsible for translating documents

j. analyzes physical evidence such as blood, hair and clothing fibres

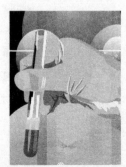

Scoring

Give yourself 1 point for each right answer.

1. i
2. g
3. f
4. j
5. e
6. d
7. a
8. h
9. c
10. b

How you rate . . .

0–2 Spy World Tourist. Thanks for stopping by.

3–5 Spy World Citizen. Welcome, we're hoping to see more of you.

6–8 Spy World Leader. We need more like you.

9–10 Spy World Ruler! The enemy is running for cover.

HONEST OR SNEAKY?

Take this spy-eye glimpse into your secret nature and find out what it reveals about your spyworthiness.

1. You observe someone take a marker from a classmate's desk, use it, then hide it. What do you do?
   a. Tell my classmate where the marker is, but not how it got there.
   b. Tell my classmate who took the marker.
   c. Tell my classmate who took the marker, unless it was my friend.
   d. Laugh maniacally as my classmate searches high and low . . .

2. You forgot to do your homework last night. What do you do?
   a. Ask my mom to write me a note with a good excuse for why I didn't do it.
   b. Write a fake excuse note "signed" by my mom.
   c. Tell my teacher I forgot to do the homework.
   d. Tell my teacher that I was abducted by alien iguanas who ate my homework.

3. You find an MP3 player on the street near your house. It works! What do you do?
   a. Show the MP3 player to all my neighbours to see if I can find the owner.
   b. Ask my friends if they know who it belongs to, then keep it if they don't.
   c. Keep the MP3 player and tell my friends I got it as a present.
   d. Keep the MP3 player but don't show it to anyone.

4. Your mom asks you if you think she looks fat. What do you tell her?
   a. The truth, gently, even if it hurts her feelings.
   b. "Of course not." I don't want to hurt her feelings.
   c. "I have no idea." And that's the truth!
   d. "Noooo, you actually look too skinny!" Maybe she'll take me out for ice cream!

5. You've been grounded for a week! But by Tuesday, your dad has forgotten about it. What do you do?
   a. Sleep over at my friend's house — or under a troll bridge — for the rest of the week in case he remembers. I always wanted to check out a troll bridge.
   b. Go play with my friends but wind up feeling guilty.
   c. Remind my dad, hoping he'll let me off the hook since I was honest about it.
   d. Stick to my punishment; I know I'm grounded, even if my dad doesn't remember.

6. A kid in your class asks to sit with you at lunch. You don't like him that much and don't really want to. What do you say to him?
   a. "Sure!" but then make myself scarce at lunch time.
   b. "I would, but I think I've got to catch up on homework in the library today."
   c. "Sure!" and then suffer through lunch.
   d. "No, I don't think so. Sorry."

7. You accidentally broke a friend's bike pump. Nobody saw you do it. What do you do?

   a. Confess right away and promise to pay for the replacement.

   b. Tell him I saw his brother break it. I've been fuelling that feud for years!

   c. Keep quiet and hope he doesn't ask me about it.

   d. Tell him I did it, but give a long explanation for why it wasn't my fault.

8. You are playing a game of shinny with a friend. The puck goes into your net, but you accidentally knock it out with your skate before he sees he's scored on you. What do you do?

   a. Nothing. If he didn't see the puck go in, well, maybe it didn't.

   b. Nothing. Tough luck for him for not seeing it.

   c. Shout, "Goal!" and congratulate him on the point.

   d. Say, "This is getting boring. Let's go jump in an alligator pond." Then throw down your hockey stick and go croc-hunting.

Scoring

1. a3 b4 c2 d1   3. a4 b3 c1 d2   5. a1 b2 c3 d4   7. a4 b1 c2 d3
2. a3 b2 c4 d1   4. a4 b2 c3 d1   6. a1 b2 c3 d4   8. a2 b1 c4 d3

How you rate . . .

8–12 The Slider. You tend to look for the easy way out. That means you might sometimes bend the truth or look the other way to avoid trouble. That's a trait spymasters avoid because it means you can't be trusted 100%.

13–20 The Waffler. You try to do the right thing, but sometimes you get confused. Should you tell the truth if it means hurting someone? If only others would make the hard decisions for you! This tendency makes you a loyal spy, but a vulnerable one. An enemy agent might convince you that their cause is the right one.

21–28 The Straight Arrow. You're a "what you see is what you get" kind of guy. Sure, sometimes you slip up, but no one's perfect. This is a pretty good trait in a spy — you're reliable, trustworthy and likely know when to keep your thoughts to yourself.

29–32 The Fanatic. You have a clear sense of right and wrong. You are certain about where you stand and what's important to you. This makes you top-notch spy material — certain of your cause, and committed to doing what it takes to stay on top.

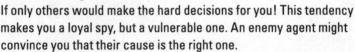

CONFIDENTIAL

WHAT'S YOUR SPY-Q: TRIVIA CHALLENGE

The history of espionage is fascinating. How well do you know your craft's storied past?

1. Who invented the cipher wheel, a device that allows you to code a message by spinning wheels with letters of the alphabet on them?
   a. Pat Sajak
   b. Ben Franklin
   c. Thomas Jefferson
   d. Frederic Cipher

2. What is the name of Great Britain's secret service?
   a. CSIS
   b. MI6
   c. NSA
   d. ROFL

3. During the American Civil War, spy Betty Duvall hid secret messages . . .
   a. in her elaborate hairdo.
   b. in the outhouse.
   c. in a teapot.
   d. in a hollowed-out pumpkin pie.

4. During World War II, a patch of land along Lake Ontario was turned into a training facility for American, British and Canadian spies. Courses included stalking techniques, martial arts and lock picking. What was the camp called?
   a. Camp Iroquoia
   b. Camp Canada
   c. Covert Camp
   d. Camp X

5. One of the oldest known codes dates from biblical times. What is it called?
   a. Atbash Code
   b. Sumerian Secret Slip
   c. Da Vinci Code
   d. Babylonian Code

6. During World War II, which "secret code" was never broken?
   a. The Navajo language, spoken by American soldiers who were Navajos.
   b. Germany's Enigma Code.
   c. An ancient Japanese dialect.
   d. England's Hedgerow Code.

7. During World War II, the famous women listed below worked for spy operations. Which one worked for the Nazis?
   a. Hedy Lamarr, an Austrian-born Hollywood star.
   b. Marlene Dietrich, a German-born Hollywood star.
   c. Josephine Baker, an American-born entertainer who lived in Paris.
   d. Coco Chanel, a French fashion designer.

8. Which famous rock band is named after a top secret spy plane?
   a. Stone Temple Pilots
   b. U2
   c. UB40
   d. Led Zeppelin

9. The word "ninja" means . . .
   a. assassin.
   b. one who steals in secretly.
   c. night walker.
   d. cat feet.

CONFIDENTIAL

10. One of the most reliable spies for the Allies during World War II was . . .
    a. a French hairdresser.
    b. a German SS officer.
    c. a ten-year-old Swiss girl.
    d. a pigeon.

Scoring

Give yourself 1 point for each correct answer.

1. c	6. a
2. b	7. d
3. a	8. b
4. d	9. a
5. a	10. d

Your spy-school report card . . .

0–3 B. New to school.

4–6 B+. B-coming better every day.

7–8 A-. Almost excellent!

9–10 A+. A is for awesome!

CONFIDENTIAL

CREATE YOUR LEGEND

Spies make up cover stories, or legends, for themselves so people won't know who they really are. Take this quiz to find out your own secret spy legend.

1. You prefer . . .

   a. music. > Go to question 2.

   b. sports. > Go to question 3.

2. You . . .

   a. are good with animals. > Go to question 4.

   b. love to travel. > Go to question 5.

3. You most enjoy . . .

   a. the high life. > Go to question 8.

   b. kicking back and relaxing. > Go to question 9.

4. Your favourite food is . . .

   a. cheese. > You are Geronimo Stilton.

   b. pie. > You are the Pied Piper of Hamelin.

   c. chicken. > Go to question 8.

5. You prefer . . .

   a. being the centre of attention. > Go to question 6.

   b. observing from the sidelines. > Go to question 7.

6. You prefer . . .

   a. singing. > You are Justin Goober.

   b. dancing. > You are Carlos Caribana.

7. You are a . . .

   a. night owl. > You are the Count.

   b. morning person. > You are the Baby Next Door.

CONFIDENTIAL

8. You prefer games that . . .

   a. are fast and full of action. > Go to question 10.

   b. require strategy. > Go to question 11.

9. You prefer . . .

   a. doing things on your own. > Go to question 13.

   b. group activities. > Go to question 14.

10. You prefer . . .

   a. hockey. > You are Tim Horton II.

   b. basketball. > You are Nicki the Knife Thrower.

   c. sailing. > You are Captain Highliner.

11. Money or power?

   a. Money. > You are Warren Tuffett.

   b. Power. > Go to question 12.

12. Which city would you prefer to live in, Ottawa or Hollywood?

   a. Ottawa. > You are Ambassador Chin.

   b. Hollywood. > You are the Bird Whisperer.

13. You prefer . . .

   a. nature. > You are Franklin the Turtle.

   b. computers. > You are the Boy Next Door.

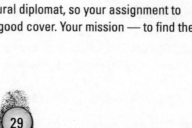

14. Which language appeals to you more?

   a. Greek. > You are Percy Jackson.

   b. Latin. > You are Principal P.U. Heiney.

You are . . .

Ambassador Chin. You are a natural diplomat, so your assignment to the national embassy in Dodo is good cover. Your mission — to find the missing dimple in your chin.

The Baby Next Door. Who would ever suspect you in this sneaky little disguise? You will have to learn how to crawl and use a sippy cup, but other than that, it's the perfect legend for uncovering your nemesis: Kid Nappy, the diabolical counter-intelligence agent who uses tiny tots as unwitting couriers by stashing secrets in their diaper linings.

The Bird Whisperer. Since you love winged creatures, your legend as a bird trainer to Hollywood's stars gives you access to suspected villain and movie producer Clint Eastwoodpecker. Remember, the early bird catches the worm.

The Boy Next Door. By day, you are mild-mannered, polite and take the garbage out for your mom. By night, you send and receive secret coded messages — upon which the fate of the world depends. At least until your mom tells you to turn your light off.

Captain Highliner. You are an excellent sailor and love fish sticks with coleslaw. With this legend, you are well placed to find the uncharted island of your arch-enemy, Dr. Fishenchips.

Carlos Caribana. Because of your natural grace and fancy footwork, your legend as a salsa teacher at a dance academy really dazzles. Dance contests take you all over the world, where you can spy on enemy agents while winning fabulous prizes.

The Count. You enjoy Gothic horror stories, so why not take on the legend that you are minor Transylvanian royalty with a love of the nightlife? Downside: you'll have to give up solid food. Upside: you get to stay up as late as you want every night, and will no longer have to go to school.

Franklin the Turtle. You are slow and steady and easy to overlook in your giant turtle disguise. Using this legend, you can gain access to the Baltimore Zoo, where arch-enemy Igor Iguana is plotting Earth's annihilation using genetically modified baby seals.

Geronimo Stilton. You are not fond of cats, but love spaghetti with lots of cheese. This legend will help you find the microfiche hidden in a computer mouse.

Justin Goober. You have a lot of charisma and musical talent. So this legend, as a teen heartthrob musical sensation, is just the $500 ticket. Upside: girls will slobber over you. Downside: girls will slobber on you.

Nicki the Knife Thrower. No one would suspect that the happy-go-lucky, fun-loving knife thrower from the Belgian Circus is a spy! Or would they? Keep your eyes peeled for suspicious activity in the contortionists' dressing room — they may have twisted priorities.

Percy Jackson. You tell people your father is a Greek god. No wonder they think you're crazy and don't take you seriously. However, insanity is the perfect cover for your covert activities at the local park, like placing messages in dead drops shaped like piles of dog doo.

Principal P.U. Heiney. You love bossing people around, so your legend as an elementary school principal is the perfect cover. You're perfectly poised to catch young sleeper agents. Unfortunately, it requires you to spend much time with children, whom you despise.

The Pied Piper of Hamelin. You are a born leader, very musical and speak fluent German (after your years of lessons, of course). This legend will help you uncover the mole in the German government's cafeteria, known as the Ratskeller.

Tim Horton II. You get to play professional hockey with this legend, so bone up on your slapshot as you practise your subterfuge. Your surveillance target: Boris Boneheadovich, star of your rival team, the Minsk Blinis.

Warren Tuffett. You have a good head for numbers, so your cover story is gazillionaire Warren Tuffet, advisor to chief economists and spiders the world over. With this legend you can follow the dirty money.

SPY VS. SPY — TRUE OR FALSE

Is the spy trivia presented here the real deal or is it counter-intelligence provided to trick you? Answer true or false.

1. In Ancient Greece a secret message might be tattooed on a courier's scalp. The courier would then let his hair grow in. To deliver the message, he shaved his head.

2. Secret messages were knitted into clothing using Morse code during World War II — a "knit" stitch was a dot, and a "purl" stitch a dash.

3. In 2010 the FBI caught Russian spies who had hidden secret messages in online photographs.

4. One of the earliest known codes was used by Julius Caesar, Emperor of Rome, and is named after him.

5. Mary, Queen of Scots was beheaded after her secret message, smuggled out of her prison in a barrel of beer, was intercepted and decoded by Queen Elizabeth's spymaster.

6. During World War I, a dog-spy training school was established in Britain.

7. In 2010 a pigeon was arrested in India, suspected of spying for Pakistan.

8. A Bulgarian dissident was once assassinated in London by a spy who poked him with a poisoned umbrella.

9. At least once, a pile of fake dog poo has been used as a dead drop to hide secret messages in plain sight.

10. The famous chef Julia Child was also a spy who invented a shark repellent.

Scoring

All are true — give yourself 1 point for each one you got right!

How you rate . . .

0–3 You Have Hidden Talent.

4–6 What's Your Secret to Success?

7–8 You've Uncovered Most of the Truth.

9–10 Who Did You Kidnap to Get All Your Correct Answers?

CONFIDENTIAL

NERVES OF STEEL
— OR SPAGHETTI?

Are you as cool as a cucumber or do you freak at the first flash of trouble? Find out how you rate in the calm-cool-and-collected department against other potential spy recruits.

1. You're sneaking a peek at your sister's diary when she walks into the room. What do you do?

    a. Calmly slide it into the drawer, flash her a big grin and say, "What's shakin', bacon?"

    b. Slam the drawer shut on my fingers and scream, "Call 911! I've cut my fingers off!" so loudly that even the neighbours come running.

    c. Hold up the diary and say, "Um, I think Mom's been sneaking a look at this — I found it in the bathroom."

2. You are walking down the street when a kid zips past you on a skateboard and crashes! What do you do?

    a. Scream, "Call 911! He's bleeding!" and run home.

    b. Laugh my head off.

    c. Rush over, make sure he's all right and help him get back on his feet.

3. Your teacher accuses you of cheating on a test. You didn't do it.

    a. I would look him dead in the eye and tell him he is mistaken.

    b. I would be too shocked and embarrassed to defend myself.

    c. I would get angry and stomp out of the classroom, shouting, "You'll be sorry for picking on *moi*, sir!"

4. You smell smoke when you are in the school washroom. It's a fire! No one else has noticed. What do you do?

    a. Pull up my pants, pull the fire alarm and calmly leave the building.

    b. Run through the halls with my fly undone, yelling, "Fire!"

    c. Stay put, frozen with fear, until a firefighter pulls up my pants for me and carries me out to safety.

5. *Two* of your crushes come up to talk to you! How do you react?

   a. I talk to them normally. They're just people. Really, really cute people.

   b. I try to flee, but run into a bunch of lockers, knocking myself out.

   c. I turn ten shades of red, but manage not to drool.

6. Which holiday would you most prefer?

   a. Hitting the half-pipe in Whistler.

   b. Chilling on Bondi Beach.

   c. Trying something new, like scuba diving in a shark cage, or surfing waves whipped up by an approaching hurricane.

7. There's a lot going on in your life. What happens at night?

   a. I have trouble falling asleep: I can't stop thinking about what's bothering me.

   b. I have nightmares about being chased by ravenous zombies waving my unfinished homework.

   c. I sleep like a log.

8. You're hiking with some friends in the bush. You stop to tie your shoe but when you stand up, everyone is gone. You're alone in the woods! What do you do?

   a. Panic and start screaming for help.

   b. Sit down on a handy tree stump and wait for my friends to find me — that's the plan we agreed to if we got separated.

   c. Start building my shelter; I've always liked the idea of spending the night on my own in the wilderness.

CONFIDENTIAL

9. It's late at night and you hear a strange noise. What do you do?
   a. Go back to sleep, hoping it was nothing.
   b. Strain my ears to hear what it is and worry — if I hear it again, I'm screaming for my momma!
   c. Get up, grab the handiest six-armed brass candelabra and go check it out.

10. You've got a sliver in your finger. What do you do?
   a. Wince and whine as my mom takes it out — I can't even look!
   b. I take it out with my teeth — no biggie.
   c. Head to my doctor's — what if it gets infected? My arm could turn green and purple and fall off. I'd be left writhing in agony, unable to write my book report, and then I'd fail English . . .

Scoring

1. a3 b1 c2	6. a2 b1 c3
2. a1 b2 c3	7. a2 b1 c3
3. a3 b2 c1	8. a1 b2 c3
4. a3 b2 c1	9. a2 b1 c3
5. a3 b1 c2	10. a2 b3 c1

How you rate . . .

10–15 Nervous Ned. You may want to try some deep breathing exercises and meditation. And that's just so the recess bell at spy school doesn't give you a heart attack!

16–22 Steely Dan. Nerves like steel, brain like tin. Ideal spy material.

23–30 Cold as Ice. Frost Power! You're ready for anything, even a move to Siberia!

CONFIDENTIAL

CAN YOU KEEP A SECRET?

Spies need to be able to keep confidential information to themselves, even under challenging conditions (can you say "water torture"?). How likely are you to keep mum when the chips are down? Answer true or false to each question.

1. People don't usually confide in me.
2. Loyalty and honesty are important qualities.
3. I really enjoy hanging out and trading news about other people with my friends.
4. I'm more of a doer than a talker.
5. I sometimes get jealous of my friends' accomplishments.
6. Being part of the cool crowd isn't something that matters much to me.
7. I shouldn't be told about things like surprise parties in advance — too much pressure!
8. I like to know things that other people don't — and keep them to myself. Knowledge is power.
9. I am so happy and excited when something nice happens to one of my friends, I can't wait to spread the news.
10. I have no trouble keeping friends.
11. I've had a fight with a friend and said something mean about him to other people.
12. I tend to get along well with everybody.
13. It's okay to add extra details to spice up a story. Everyone does it.
14. People trust me with their feelings.
15. I get cross and spiteful when I don't get my way.
16. People think of me as a "stand-up guy."
17. I sometimes blurt things out before I think them through.

18. I am level-headed.
19. Sneaking a peek at a friend's test is okay if I'm just checking my answers.
20. I don't usually brag about myself — I prefer to keep my accomplishments to myself.

Scoring

Add up your FALSE answers for all the ODD numbered questions:

_____

Add up your TRUE answers for all the EVEN numbered questions:

_____

Add the two totals together for your score: _____

How you rate . . .

0–4 Blabbermouth. You may be able to keep a secret of your own till the cows come home, but others' secrets? Not so much. Remember, spies need to be 100% trustworthy, and so do you.

5–10 Hidden Depths. You sometimes let enthusiasm get the better of you and speak without thinking. That means you might not be the best secret-keeper going. Practise slowing down your mouth a bit and think about what you want to say — you don't want to spill the secret beans and get the world blown up!

11–16 Your Lips Are Sealed. People like you because you are easy to get along with and don't give off lots of attitude. You are discreet with private information and avoid spreading rumours or talking smack. You'll have access to the nation's most top-secret secrets in no time!

17–20 Silent as the Grave. You never give anything away. You keep your thoughts and feelings to yourself. You file away everything you learn about other people deep in the back of your brain. No one will pry the detailed assault plan from your locked lips!

CONFIDENTIAL

ARE YOU FIT TO BE A SPY?

Are you super-spy tough or couch-potato material? We come in all different shapes and sizes, but it's always important to be fit. That goes double for potential double agents! To find out how you stack up, do each of the tests that follow. Then add up your points to get an overall spy-fit total.

Note: If you are not familiar with these activities, or if you do not exercise regularly, do these tests with adult supervision.

Test 1

Upper-Body Strength — THE HE-MAN HEAVE HO
You're crawling through the air ducts on your belly when the building you're in collapses! Can you push your way out of the rubble?

The Test
You will be doing push-ups. Lie face down on the floor. Put your palms down, just below your shoulders. Keeping your body straight like a plank, push into the floor with your arms to raise yourself up. Do not arch your back or bend your knees. Lock your stomach muscles. Do as many push-ups as you can, without losing the proper form, in 1 minute.

Scoring

Refer to the chart below. If you are older than 10, subtract 1 from your total number of push-ups for every year that you are older. If you are younger than 10, add 1 push-up for every year that you are younger. For example, if you are 12 and did 18 push-ups, take away 2 to give you a score of 16. If you are 8 years old and did 18 push-ups, add 2 to your points to give you a total of 20. Look up your points below, then write them down and add them to your points from the activities that follow.

Push-Ups	Rating	Points
Less than 5	Pancake	4
6–16	Almost Orange Crush!	6
17–27	Skyscraper Raiser!	8
28+	Super Spy!	10

Test 2

Upper-Body Strength — THE SNAKE PIT ESCAPE

Can you pull yourself out of a seething nest of serpents or will you be vanquished by the vipers?

You will need:
- A friend
- A stopwatch or a clock with a second hand
- A "chin-up bar" or other horizontal bar placed high enough so that your feet will be off the floor as you pull up. It should be secure and strong enough to hold you.

The Test
You will be doing chin-ups. Begin by hanging from the bar, using an underhand grip. Using only your arms — do not kick or jerk your body — pull yourself up toward the bar. Your chin should be able to go above the bar. Do as many chin-ups as you can, without losing your form (kicking or jerking your body), in 1 minute.

Scoring
Refer to the chart below. If you are older than 10, take away 1 chin-up for every year older you are. If you are younger than 10, add 1 chin-up for every year. Add your points to those from the other activities.

Chin-Ups	Rating	Points
Less than 2	Snake Food	4
3–8	Survived By a Hair!	6
9–14	With One Hand Tied Behind Your Back!	8
15+	Super Spy!	10

Test 3

Core Strength — THE IMPROMPTU WATER-SKI CHASE
The enemy is escaping by boat! You step on two slats from the damaged pier, swing a dog leash around the boat's cleat and let the escaping craft pull you along on your "water skis." Are your abs tough enough to help you withstand this absolutely bizarre form of water torture?

You will need:
• A friend
• A stopwatch or a clock with a second hand

The Test
You will be doing sit-ups. Lie on your back with your hands clasped behind your head. Be careful not to use your hands to pull your head up: they should just be there to lightly support it. Bend your knees and put the soles of your feet on the floor. Your heels should be no more than 30 cm from your bum. On "Go," curl your torso up until your elbows touch your knees. Do as many sit-ups as you can in 1 minute.

Scoring
Refer to the chart below. If you are older than 10, subtract 2 sit-ups for every year that you are older. If you are younger than 10, add 2. Add your points to those from the other activities.

Sit-Ups	Rating	Points
Less than 10	Sunk!	4
11–25	Able to Rely on Those Abs of Steel	6
26–36	Absolutely Amazing	8
37+	Super Spy!	10

Aerobic Fitness — THE DASH TO THE NUKE BUTTON

The enemy has set a nuke to explode in less than 10 minutes. You're 2500 metres away. Can you reach the bomb and deactivate it before your own ticker gives out?

You will need:
- A stopwatch or a clock with a second hand
- A jump rope, if you wish

The Test
You will need to run in place, jump rope or do jumping jacks for 3 minutes. At the end of the 3 minutes, you will describe how you feel.

Scoring
Refer to the chart below. Add your points to those from the other activities.

How You Feel	Rating	Points
Stopped before 3 minutes were up	Kaboom!	4
Heart pounding; exhausted	Collapsed on the Button and Saved the World!	6
A little breathless, but okay	Reached the Button With Seconds to Spare!	8
Barely broke a sweat	Super Spy!	10

CONFIDENTIAL

Test 5

Balance Test — THE RACE TO DEFUSE THE BOMB

You've spotted a ticking bomb wedged between two ceiling tiles, but you can only reach it if you stand on one leg and stretch your arms above your head. Can you stay steady enough to defuse the device or will you wobble and wind up waving bye-bye to the world?

You will need:
- A friend
- A stopwatch or clock with a second hand

The Test
Close your eyes and stretch your arms above your head. Lift one leg off the floor by bending it at the knee. Remain standing on the other leg as long as possible. Repeat 2 more times. Then do the test 3 times on the other foot, too. Get your friend to time how long you can stand for.

Scoring
Using your best time, refer to the chart below.

Time	Rating	Points
Less than 12 seconds	Kaboom!	4
12–23 seconds	Wobbled, But Whew!	6
24–29 seconds	Steady as a Stork	8
30+ seconds	Super Spy!	10

CONFIDENTIAL

Overall Scoring

Add up your points from each of the five fitness tests. Compare your total to the scores here.

How you rate . . .

20–28 Desk Job. Even if you're not yet sold on being a spy, you would benefit from more activity in your day. It's important to find something you like — maybe being part of a baseball or soccer team would get you out more. Or maybe you'd prefer something more solitary, like running or bike riding. Get active for at least 10 minutes at a time, 4 times a day and at least you'll be able to outrun the bad guys!

30–38 Primed for Field Action. Your fitness level is good. You can build strength and stamina by playing a wider variety of sports and practising your skills every day. Work up a sweat for at least 20 minutes, 3 times a day to increase your fitness power and ensure better success as a spy on assignment.

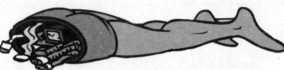

40–46 Part Man, Part Machine. You possess above-average strength and stamina. Add to your skill set by continuing to develop your aerobic fitness and strength — do at least 30 minutes of aerobic exercise daily. But don't ignore your human side: try yoga to develop flexibility and inner strength.

48–50 Super-Spy Athlete. You've got excellent strength and stamina. Build on this solid base by increasing the time you engage in physical activity to an hour or more every day. You'll do great as a field operative, no matter what the physical challenge — strength, speed or snakes!

CONFIDENTIAL

MEMORY CHALLENGE

Spies need to have an excellent eye for detail and an even better memory. Some of the questions below will ask you about information that appears earlier in the book. If you cheat (that means you look for the answer before answering the question), you automatically fail the test!

1. Do you know your best friend's birthday?
   a. Yes
   b. No

2. What animal is pictured on page 17 (the quiz about spy slang)?
   a. Cat
   b. Pigeon
   c. Mole

3. What are the names of the planets, in order, beginning with the closest to the sun?

4. Which of these three pictures does NOT appear anywhere else in this book?

b.   c.

5. Which fictional spy character is NOT named in this book?
   a. Dr. Evil
   b. Alex Rider
   c. Nick Fury

6. The Table of Contents lists how many quizzes?
   a. 29
   b. 30
   c. 25

7. On page 28 there is a picture of a person playing an instrument. What is it?
   a. A violin.
   b. A guitar.
   c. A kazoo.

8. In which quiz does the word "cucumber" appear?
   a. Which Fictional Spy Villain Are You?
   b. Spy vs. Spy
   c. Nerves of Steel — or Spaghetti?

9. Do you remember your score for the FIRST quiz you took in this book?
   a. Yes
   b. No

10. What was the first question in this quiz? Don't look!
    a. I know the answer.
    b. I don't remember the answer.
    c. I looked.

Scoring

Give yourself 1 point for each correct answer below, except for question 3.

1. a

2. c

3. Mercury, Venus, Earth, Mars, Jupiter, Saturn, Uranus, Neptune (score 1 point for each correct planet name; score 5 additional points for getting them in the correct order).

4. b

5. c

6. b

7. b

8. c

9. a

10. a (if you chose c, you fail!)

How you rate . . .

0–5 Forget It. Your mind is like a steel trap. Without the steel. Or the trap.

6–17 Memory Maven. You've got a solid grasp of the past and strong observation skills. Remember to apply for spy school — you'll be a shoo-in!

18–22 Photographic Memory. You have a mind like a lock box — what goes in, stays in! With mental skills like these you'll be a member of the Super Spy Elite Club!

CONFIDENTIAL

CAN YOU DECODE TEACHERSPEAK?

Being a spy means being able to understand what people are saying, even if they are using a code. Teachers are notorious code-talkers. Match the Teacherspeak code phrases on the left with what the teachers are really saying on the right.

Teacherspeak

1. It's time to do some independent reading now.

2. We're starting an exciting new unit!

3. The test will be easy.

4. Tell me what happened.

5. The next person to make a peep will get detention!

6. You're the best class I ever had.

7. What an improvement!

8. You're so good at expressing yourself.

9. Can I have a volunteer?

10. What did you say?

11. Did you do your homework last night?

12. What a busy day it's been!

13. I'll think about it.

14. Do you want to go to the principal's office?

15. I bet you're all looking forward to summer vacation.

16. Your art project is so creative!

Meaning

a. No.

b. You're the best class I've ever had.

c. You're really getting it! Unless your mom did it for you.

d. You so didn't do your homework last night.

e. Boy can you ever talk!

f. How will I sort this one out?

g. This is your last chance, buster.

h. I have such a headache.

i. I have no idea what that's supposed to be.

j. Sigh, most of you are probably not going to love graphing . . .

k. Beach, here I come!

l. When will this day end?

m. Okay, I'll choose . . . YOU.

n. Work on your own so I can get my marking done and hit the gym.

o. If you're smart, you'll take that back.

p. If you spent the last week studying for it. *Mwa-ha-haa!*

Scoring

Give yourself 1 point for each right answer.

1. n	9. m
2. j	10. o
3. p	11. d
4. f	12. l
5. h	13. a
6. b	14. g
7. c	15. k
8. e	16. i

How you rate . . .

0–4 Novice Decoder. Do you often find yourself confused when speaking with your teachers? Pay attention to body language, not just the words people say, to better develop your decoding skills.

5–8 Level II Decoder. You've got the basics down. Before long you may just understand your parents, too!

9–12 Advanced Placement. You have an excellent grasp of Teacherspeak. You might consider a career as a principal instead of a spy.

13–16 Super Decoder. Go to the head of the class. There is nothing left to teach you.

CONFIDENTIAL

YOUR MISSION, SHOULD YOU CHOOSE TO ACCEPT IT . . .

Intelligence has confirmed an enemy spy is operating in Ottawa. You arrive there, hoping your source will make contact and provide further details. Your mission is to uncover the spy and his operation. You get to choose the direction your mission takes. Will it be a smashing success or a great-big flop?

1. You're walking to your hotel when someone brushes up against you. You discover they have put something in your pocket. What is it?

    a. I dunno, but it's ticking! > Go to question 2.

    b. A photograph of the Eiffel Tower. > Go to question 3.

    c. A coded message. > Go to question 4.

2. Your pocket is ticking!

    a. You quickly toss your coat down a manhole. > Go to 5.

    b. You calmly look inside and turn off the gizmo. > Go to 6.

3. You take the photo as a clue to go to the French embassy. There, you notice a strangely shaped fire hydrant. You approach it and discover it is a dead drop. Inside there appears to be a computer card.

    a. You insert the card into your mini-computer and discover it has the plans for a major build-up of the Martian army. > Go to 12.

    b. You sniff it. It smells yummy. You eat it. > Go to 13.

4. You use your handy-dandy decoder to reveal the secret. What does the message say?

    a. *Help! My family is being folded into fortune cookies!* > Go to 21.

    b. *Sale on Men's "X-Large Red Shoes, One Day Only!* > Go to 20.

    c. *Say cheese!* > Go to 29.

5. The manhole explodes! You look around and see a suspiciously dressed clown slipping into a hardware store.

   a. You take off your shoe to call headquarters. > Go to 7.

   b. You follow the clown. > Go to 8.

6. Once the gizmo is off, you discover it is made by Ace Hardware and Coyote Wrasslers Inc. You notice the store is across the street.

   a. You go into the store and ask for the owner. > Go to 8.

   b. You go buy a coyote. > Go to 9.

7. Headquarters tells you to follow the clown! But he's gone!

   a. You look up *Clowns* in the phone book. > Go to 15.

   b. You look for balloon animal tracks and follow them into a hardware store. > Go to 8.

8. In the hardware store, you notice a secret doorway.

   a. You go through it. > Go to 16.

   b. You ask the hardware store owner if he's seen a clown. The owner takes out a rocket launcher and points it at you. > Go to 17.

9. There is more to this coyote than meets the eye! What is it?

   a. The coyote's an enemy agent! It eats you! > So sorry, you have failed your mission. Better luck next time, Mr. Lunch!

   b. The coyote's really a clown-tracking bloodhound. > Go to 16.

10. You follow the smell to the basement where you find Ratso Ricard, the notorious French double agent, making double-cream brie! You sit down, share some brie and decide to work for the other side because they have better cheese than we do. Mission fail.

11. When you order the cheese, the proprietor hands you another coded message. It says, *Thank you for reading this message. While you were reading it, we searched your face with identification recognition software. We have determined that you are a Canadian secret agent. Your cover is blown. Have a free chunk of Gruyère, courtesy of your enemy.* Mission fail.

12. Martians? Clearly, this whole adventure is a prank! You throw away the chip and go about your business. The next day, Earth is invaded by Martians. Mission fail.

13. It turns out to be macadamia-nut cheese, a rare and expensive delicacy only made in Hawaii. The nutty, cheesy deliciousness wows you and knocks any thought of espionage out of your mind. All you care about is getting more of this fabulous cheese! You decide to move to Hawaii and live the rest of your life on the beach making, eating and cutting the cheese. Mission fail, but it's all good.

14. If you wound up at this question, you are seriously challenged with following directions. Mission fail.

15. You find a coded message under *Clowns*. What does it say?

a. *Please save my family! They are being held by evil clowns in a fortune cookie factory!* > Go to 21.

b. *Watch out for the little old lady feeding the pigeons by the museum. She is really Zada Finke, the Bulgarian spy bent on destroying Canada.* > Go to 24.

16. You go through a doorway and find yourself behind the hardware store. You discover the clown's costume in a trash bin. From the corner of your eye you see a firefighter scaling a skyscraper.

    a. You chase the firefighter using your special spidey grips, which you have conveniently stashed in your hat, and stop him. > Go to 19.

    b. You notice a fire on the third floor of the building and see a little old lady going into the stairwell carrying a gas can. She's the arsonist! You follow her. > Go to 24.

17. You turn on your automatic rocket launcher deactivator which you have conveniently stashed in your hat. The hardware store owner crumbles and tells you the clown is really Dirk Dunderhead, your arch-enemy. He is planning to use poisoned gingersnaps to zombify and enslave the populace.

    a. You buy a hammer. > Go to 18.

    b. You quickly rig up a loudspeaker using items from the store. You use it to warn the city and save the world. > Mission accomplished!

18. Unfortunately, the clown is right behind you and uses a bigger hammer to knock you unconscious. He poisons the city and your mission fails. So sorry, Agent Zombie!

19. The fire turns out to be real. You are arrested for interfering with official business. So sorry, mission fail.

CONFIDENTIAL

20. You go to the shoe store and find it is really a front for a criminal enterprise: an international espionage ring disguised as a circus.

  a. You secretly snap pictures of all the employees with the camera you have cleverly stashed in your hat. > Go to 28.

  b. You buy a clown suit at a really great price. > Go to 27.

21. You find your way to Lee Hai Spy Cookie Factory. You climb up the fire escape and into a window. Inside, you find a family of werewolves tied with silver chains. They tell you they are victims of a mutant experiment run by the psycho-clown scientist Frodo Frankfurter.

  a. You release them. > Go to 23.

  b. You ignore them while you look around the premises and find a computer room. Inside is a droopy-faced clown you recognize as Frodo! > Go to 22.

22. Place the psycho-clown scientist in a headlock and call for backup. Mission accomplished!

23. Alas, they were lying. They attack you and turn you into one of their own. So sorry, Wolfie. Mission fail.

24. You follow the little old lady to the steps of a museum. There, she begins talking to two small children.

  a. You dash in, tackle the little old lady and rescue the children. > Go to 25.

  b. You wait and observe. You realize the children are actually very short Bulgarian mobsters — Zada Finke and Frodo Baddi! You call headquarters for further instructions. > Go to 26.

25. The little old lady was a double agent working for your side! The two small children were actually Zada Finke and Frodo Baddi in disguise! They take you and your fellow agent to a pasta factory and turn you both into fettuccine alfredo. Mission fail.

CONFIDENTIAL

26. Headquarters says, "Wait for backup!" A moment later, five helicopters, two tanks and sixteen police cars swoop in, capture the mobsters and save Canada. Mission accomplished!

27. You realize that your life-long dream is to be a clown, not a secret agent. You quit the agency and start calling yourself Boodleheimer the Bodacious. Before long, you are a famous and rich comedian with a pad in Beverly Hills and a Lamborghini that shoots water from its flower-shaped headlights.

28. You send the pictures to headquarters. The perpetrators are quickly identified as a terrorist cell bent on world destruction through bad jokes. You heckle them into submission. Mission accomplished!

29. You go to the nearby French cheese store.

    a. You smell a rat. > Go to 10.

    b. You order a cheese called French Spy. > Go to 11.

CONFIDENTIAL

SILLY SPY QUIZ

1. Which animal is really the spy in the jungle?
   a. A chameleon.
   b. A spider.
   c. A llama.

2. What spy might you find on your face?
   a. A mole.
   b. An eye-dentifier.
   c. A stray nose hair.

3. What is a spy's favourite type of food?
   a. Anything spicy!
   b. Mince pie.
   c. Seafood.

4. What do spies call twins?
   a. Double trouble.
   b. Double agents.
   c. Twosies.

5. Where did the spies rendezvous?
   a. Hernando's Hideaway.
   b. A butcher shop.
   c. Dew Drop Inn.

6. Which is the worst place to have a spy operation's headquarters?
   a. At a beach.
   b. At a bowling alley.
   c. At a hospital.

7. Where does a spy work best?
   a. In bed.
   b. On a roof.
   c. In the subway.

8. Which part of your body is best at espionage?
   a. Your eyes.
   b. Your liver.
   c. Your spine.

9. Which spy is best at math?
   a. A double agent.
   b. Double-oh-seven.
   c. Dr. No.

10. Why are spies sick a lot?
    a. They tend to catch codes.
    b. They need frequent operations.
    c. They don't wear underwear.

CONFIDENTIAL

Scoring

Give yourself 1 point for each right answer.
Add them up to get your results.

1. c — What's a llama doing in the jungle if he isn't spying?

2. a

3. a — Get it? *Spy*-cy! Unless they are British, then b.

4. b

5. b — It was the perfect place to *meat*!

6. b — Too easy to be pinned down!

7. a — It's undercover!

8. c — Get it? *Spy*-ne?

9. b

10. b

How you rate . . .

0–3 Kidding Kid! Your spy skills are a real joke.

4–6 Sly Spy. You can pick locks with that sharp wit!

7–8 Hilari-espionage. You are the spymaster of silliness.

9–10 Legendary. You are the king of counter-intelligence and terrible puns.

BREAK THE CODE (EASY)

One of the earliest codes ever used was a substitution code. To create one, letters of the alphabet are replaced with new letters using a simple pattern. For example, you shift each letter of the alphabet by one, as shown below.

ABCDEFGHIJKLMNOPQRSTUVWXYZ (original alphabet)
BCDEFGHIJKLMNOPQRSTUVWXYZA (new alphabet)

When you write a coded message you substitute a letter from the original alphabet with one from the new one. A becomes B, G becomes H, T becomes U, etc. So the word "CAT" would be spelled "DBU."

To decode the message, simply match the letter from the new alphabet to the original alphabet: "DBU" becomes "CAT."

See if you can decode the following secret messages using this substitution code.

1. ZPV HPU JU!

_____

2. UIF OFYU BOTXFS TIJGUT MFUUFST CZ UXP QMBDFT, TP B CFDPNFT D, BOE TP PO.

_____

3. FKF AQW HKIWTG KV QWV? PKEG YQTM!

_____

4. YCCCC JCCCCC JCCCCC!

_____

5. VJKU DQQM KU YCVEJKPI AQW!

_____

59

CONFIDENTIAL

Scoring

Give yourself 1 point for each right answer.

1. YOU GOT IT!
2. THE NEXT ANSWER SHIFTS LETTERS BY TWO PLACES, SO A BECOMES C, AND SO ON.
3. DID YOU FIGURE IT OUT? NICE WORK!
4. WAAAA HAAAAA HAAAAA!
5. THIS BOOK IS WATCHING YOU!

How you rate . . .

0–1 GBC! With practise, you may get better . . .

2–3 HSFBU! Before you know it, you'll be dreaming in code.

4 BXFTPNF! The Secret Message Department of the CIA will be calling you.

5 YQY! Time to invent your own codes — you are too clever for us.

CONFIDENTIAL

BREAK THE CODE
(A LITTLE HARDER)

A trickier kind of substitution code uses key words to shift the letters of the alphabet. For example, if the key word is CODE, the shifted alphabet would look like this

ABCDEFGHIJKLMNOPQRSTUVWXYZ(original alphabet)
CODEABCDEFGHIJKLMNOPQRSTUV(new alphabet)

In this keyed code, A becomes C, G also becomes C. This is what makes this code doubly tricky — some letters can have two possible matches. Imagine if you didn't know the key word! So the word CAT, coded, would be spelled DCP.

To decode the message, simply match the letter from the new alphabet to the letter from original alphabet: DCP becomes CAT or HGT. Can you figure out which of the two is right? Of course, you can!

See if you can decode the following secret messages using this key substitution code.

A	B	C	D	E	F	G	H	I	J	K	L	M	N	O	P	Q	R	S	T	U	V	W	X	Y	Z
C	O	D	E	A	B	C	D	E	F	G	H	I	J	K	L	M	N	O	P	Q	R	S	T	U	V

1. EK UKQ DCRA C EKJ GAU?

_____

2. SDCP COKQP C IKJ GAU?

_____

3. GAAL QL PDA CKKE SKNG.

_____

61

CONFIDENTIAL

4. UKQ OAAI PK OA GAAJ KJ DKEAO.

_____

5. E DCRA JK DHQA SDCP PDEO OCUO.

_____

Scoring

Give yourself 1 point for each correct answer.

1. Do you have a don key?
2. What about a mon key?
3. Keep up the good work.
4. You seem to be keen on codes.
5. I have no clue what this says.

How you rate . . .

1 JEDA! You're practically a Jedi of Code.

2–3 OICNPEA! A Yoda of Coda.

4 SKK DKK! You're a code contender!

5 C-LHQO! No code can stump you!

PICTURE-PUZZLE CODE

Can you suss out the secret meanings of these tricky picture codes?

1 SECRET ↑

2  4 cover

3 9 7 1 U 5 3

4  J (AN) B

5 ✓ SAFE ✗ SORRY

CONFIDENTIAL

6 SECOND TIMING

7 <u>BLACK</u>
COAT

8 i✓i

9 LOOK

10 CHAR**ACT**ER

Scoring

Give yourself 1 point for each correct answer.

1. Top secret!
2. Head for cover
3. The odds are against you
4. An inside job
5. Better safe than sorry
6. Split second timing
7. Black overcoat
8. Right between the eyes
9. Look inside
10. Act out of character

How you rate . . .

0–3 Puzzling. Bet you were just getting the hang of it.

4–7 Puzzler. You've got a knack for

"THINKING ⬚ "

8–10 Puzzled. You are one with the puzzles!

BREAK THE CODE (HARDEST)

All the codes below are simple substitution codes without key words. But what have we substituted for each letter? Now that's our little secret! Can you figure out what has been substituted for each letter to break each code?

1. 25-15-21'-18-5 14-21-13-2-5-18 15-14-5. [Hint:15=O]

_____

2. DZGXS BLFI YZXP. [Hint: P=K]

_____

3. ZPV BSF TPPPP SJHIU. [Hint: W=V]

_____

4. CNM'S FDS KDES ADGHMC. [Hint: W=X]

_____

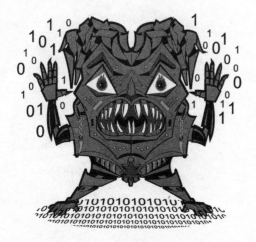

CONFIDENTIAL

Scoring

Give yourself 1 point for each correct answer.

1. Each number represents a letter's place in the alphabet. A = 1, b = 2, etc. The message reads, "You're number one."

2. The coded alphabet is written back to front — a=z, b=y, c=x, etc. The message reads, "Watch your back."

3. The letters have been shifted one position to the right, like the first code in this book. The message reads, "You are soooo right."

4. The letters in this code have been shifted one position to the left. The message reads, "Don't get left behind."

How you rate . . .

1 Junior Cryptologist. Paying your dues!

2–3 Senior Cryptologist. They call you in for the tough codes.

4 The Cryptolo-genius! Your codes are unbreakable! Even to you!

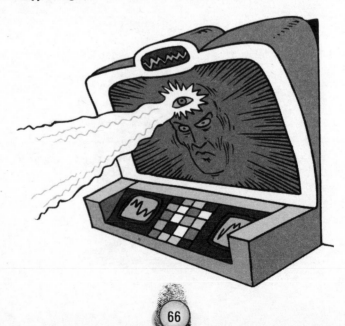

CONFIDENTIAL

SPY LOGIC PUZZLE TEST

Spies need to be very clear-headed, logical and able to look at things in different ways so they can solve problems on the fly. Can you solve these logic problems taken from the spy-school entry exam?

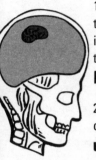

1. What letter can be inserted into each of the three letter groups below to turn them into words, without changing the order of the letters?

HVE   GE   BG

2. What is the fourth word that would complete this set?

up   down   tall _____

3. Complete this sentence:

ten is to twelve as _____ is to eight.

4. What three-letter word, if added to the end of these letter combinations, would turn all of them into words?

Br_____   downt_____   fl_____

5. What word does NOT belong in this set:

Teal   Scarlet   Indigo   Razzle   Olive

6. What comes next?

A K Q __

7. Fill in the missing letters:

Do re __ __ __ __ __ do

CONFIDENTIAL

8. Each word in this ladder is only one letter different from the words above and below it. Fill in the missing words to complete the ladder.

HAIL
WAIL

_____

WANT

_____

WIND

9. Which of the words here does not have a homonym?

Bear   Witch   Seen   Fail   Fair

10. Think of three words ending in gry. Angry and hungry are two of them. There are three words in the English language. What is the third word? The word is something everyone uses every day. If you have read carefully, you will have already seen it.

Scoring

1 point for each correct answer.

1. A (HAVE AGE BAG)

2. short

3. 6

4. own

5. razzle, all the rest are colours.

6. J. These are the symbols on playing cards, beginning with the A for Ace. The next cards are King, Queen and Jack.

7. mi, fa, so, la, ti. These are the notes of the musical scale, in ascending order.

8. WAIT; WAND

9. Fail. Bear=Bare; Witch=Which; Seen=Scene; Fair =Fare.

10. language. It is the third word in "the English language."

How you rate . . .

0–2 Stretch a Little Next Time.
3–5 Spy-Q of a Genius.
6–8 Agent Brainiac.
9–10 Smarter Than Spy-enstein!

CONFIDENTIAL

YOUR SECOND MISSION, SHOULD YOU CHOOSE TO ACCEPT IT

You are on top of a mountain in the Swiss Alps, waiting for your contact from Bellawalrus. He has important information about enemy mutant dolphin movements in the Black Sea. What happens next?

1. You see a man in expensive ski clothes coming toward you.

   a. So? You are at a posh ski resort. Everyone is wearing expensive ski clothes. > Go to question 2.

   b. You believe it could be Boris Natasha — the evil agent of Dr. Somebodyorother. > Go to question 3.

   c. You check your phone for photos of your contact and it's a match: the skier is your contact John Smith. > Go to question 4.

2. The man skis by you and you notice he is wearing a strange backpack. It resembles a bomb you once made in shop class. You . . .

   a. decide to ski after him. > Go to 5.

   b. shake off your foolish fancy and order another root beer from the chalet menu. > Go to 6.

3. You decide to go after Boris Natasha. As you ski down the mountain, you notice another man wearing a suspicious backpack shaped like a teddy bear. You . . .

   a. decide to follow the man with the suspicious backpack. > Go to 5.

   b. ignore the man with the backpack and keep going after the man you think is Boris Natasha. > Go to 7.

4. You follow your contact, John Smith, down the mountain. You run smack into a class of toddlers on the bunny slope. You lose sight of Smith! You . . .

a. stop to pick up the toddlers you knocked over in your haste. As you do, you see Smith in the parking lot below, getting into an SUV. You follow Smith and get into the car. > Go to 16.

b. ignore the crying toddlers sprawled in the snow and ski after Smith! You catch up to him just as he gets on a T-bar leading to the top of the mountain — the dreaded Dead Man Run. You follow. > Go to 20.

5. The man with the backpack is fast. He leads you down some bumpy, double-black-diamond slopes and into a wooded section of the mountain. You . . .

a. keep up with him no problem. > Go to 7.

b. fall on your face. > Go to 8.

6. A few minutes later, you hear a thunderous roar. Avalanche! You . . .

a. stay where you are so you won't miss your contact. Plus, you want another root beer. > Go to 25.

b. immediately ski out of the chalet to see what's going on. You discover half of the mountain has collapsed. Sticking out of the snow, you see a pair of legs with pink ski boots. You pull the person out just before she suffocates and you discover she is your contact, Candy Kane. > Go to 10.

7. You arrive in a quiet, isolated glade. The skier is there. He removes his ski mask and you realize it is Boris Natasha, the notorious enemy agent! You . . .

a. immediately remove the stun gun you have hidden in your pants and blast him one. > Go to 9.

b. wait to see what he does. > Go to 11.

CONFIDENTIAL

8. Falling on your face was a brilliant move — it saved you when the bomb in the suspicious backpack exploded and caused an avalanche further down the mountain. Now you . . .

   a. ski into the thick of the avalanche and rescue 200 people, including the person who had the bomb. It turns out to be Sonya Snopes, a well-known Hollywood terrorist, in disguise (she had thrown the bomb into a gorge before it exploded). > Go to 26.

   b. ski to the bottom of the mountain and take the next chair lift back to the top to meet your contact as planned. > Go to 17.

9. Alas, if you had been a tad more patient, you would have discovered he was about to switch sides. But now, when he recovers from the blast, he cannot talk and the stun gun has paralyzed him! And you missed your rendezvous with your contact. Mission fail.

10. What does Candy Kane do next?

    a. Gives you the confidential information she has smuggled out of Bellawalrus in her fake nose. You brush the snow off her and wave goodbye as she skis into the sunset. > Go to 12.

    b. Tells you she was spotted by the enemy agent Hoo Hoo Ha from the Republic of Lafta. She threw the secret documents into the toilet at the chalet. > Go to 15.

11. Patience works in your favour! Boris says he wishes to switch sides. He has thousands of documents on a flash drive he has secreted inside his capacious belly button. You arrange for him to be conducted to a safe house, nip back to the chalet to make your rendezvous with your contact and come out of this mission a success. Mission accomplished!

CONFIDENTIAL

12. You read the documents from Candy. They're fakes! You . . .

   a. ski after her. > Go to 13.

   b. shrug your shoulders and go home. > Go to 14.

13. You catch up to Candy in a chocolate store at the bottom of the hill. She is sharing a truffle with Boris Natasha! You . . .

   a. stun them both with the stun gun you had hidden in your ski hat and tie them together with the lasso you have hidden in your pants. You leave them in the woods for the Big Bad Wolf — an assassin you know and love (except for his breath) — to take care of.
   > Go to 18.

   b. call headquarters for backup!
   > Go to 19.

14. So sorry. You were so close, but you gave up too soon. Remember, perseverance is as important in spy work as in life! Mission fail.

15. You go back to the chalet and use the handy dandy plunger you have stashed under your ski hat to bring the secret documents back up out of the clogged toilet. Mission accomplished!

16. In the car, your contact gives you the dolphin movements. You stash them under your hat and return to the ski hill. You've bought a full-day ski pass, after all! Mission accomplished.

17. You are waiting outside the chalet for your contact when you see a child dressed in a ballet tutu and tiara go in. What do you realize?

   a. The child is Boris Natasha in disguise! > Go to 23.

   b. Your mother and sister have arrived for their annual ski holiday — why did they have to pick your mountain? > Go to 24.

18. Mission accomplished!

CONFIDENTIAL

19. Headquarters sends its Top Secret Enemy Immobilization Force. They surround the mountain and bombard it with pepper spray. All the skiers on the hill start sneezing, and Boris and Candy, who are both allergic to pepper, surrender. Mission accomplished!

20. At the top of Dead Man Run, John Smith hands you the secret information he has hidden in a can of sardines. He tells you there's more — he has spotted enemy agent Boris Natasha on the mountain! You . . .

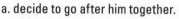

a. decide to go after him together.
> Go to 21.
b. say, "Thanks for the fish!" Then you take the secret docs back to headquarters as instructed. > Go to 22.

21. You and Smith ski down the mountain in complicated swoops and turns. You out-ski Boris Natasha and are waiting for him at the bottom of the mountain when he arrives. You and Smith handcuff Boris with the cuffs you have cleverly stashed in your ski hat. Mission accomplished, AND you get promoted to spymaster!

22. Mission accomplished, though when you get back to headquarters, they tell you John Smith has single-handedly captured Boris Natasha and has been promoted. Smith will now be your boss. His first act is to fire you for failing to spot an important opportunity. You don't mind though, because you've already decided you would rather be a ski instructor.

23. You follow Boris into the girl's washroom. There, you remove the stun gun you have cleverly stashed in your ski boot. You immobilize Boris, tie his hands and feet with an improvised set of handcuffs you've woven out of toilet paper, and leave him there while you go back to successfully meet up with your contact. Mission accomplished!

24. Your mother spots you and calls you over, asking you if you've done your homework. She says you have ketchup on your cheek and pulls a tissue out of her bag to wipe it off. She leaves the used tissue on the table and she and your sister go off to the washroom. You look at the used tissue and discover that it has the secret movements of enemy dolphins on it. Your mother is your contact! Mission accomplished.

25. Your contact shows up. It is Sam Widch, your childhood sweetheart! You get the documents and convince Sam to marry you. Mission accomplished.

26. The bad news: you failed in your mission to meet your contact and get the secret information. The good news: you succeeded in nabbing an enemy from your agency's most wanted list and became a Swiss hero to boot. Nice work!

SPOT THE SPY

Each of the pictures on the next few pages shows a snapshot of a place. Can you use your keen powers of observation to spot the spy in each picture?

1.

2.

3.

4.

5.

6.

7.

8.

Scoring

Give yourself 1 point for each right answer.

1. On the ground to the right of the tallest tree.
2. On the sidewalk, against the bricks.
3. In a window in the tallest building, four storeys up.
4. To the right of the third set of bottom floor windows.
5. The last house on the right, on the right side of the garage.
6. Top right corner, on the roof.
7. Top right corner, in the tree.
8. Bottom of the left tree's trunk.

How you rate . . .

0–2 The Spy Could Be Beside You!

3–5 The Spy Has Met His Match.

6–8 The Spy Doesn't Stand a Chance Against Your Eagle Eyes!

LOGIC PUZZLES FROM
THE SPY-SCHOOL ENTRY EXAM

1. Your sock drawer contains ten pairs of white socks and ten pairs of black socks. You may only take out one sock at a time and you can't see the colour of the sock until you've taken it. How many socks do you have to take before you're guaranteed to have a pair?

2. A cricket is trying to jump up a riverbank that is 60 cm high. Every minute, the cricket jumps up 3 cm but slips back 2. How long does it take the cricket to make it over the top?

3. You are given a corked bottle with a coin inside it. You may not remove the cork from the bottle. You may not break the bottle. How will you get the coin out?

4. What gets wetter the more it dries?

5. Give me food and I will live. Give me water and I will die. What am I?

6. There are two pairs of letters missing from the following word. Both pairs are identical. What pair of letters can you insert to complete the whole word? _ _**rses**_ _**e**

7. Add letters to the front and back of this letter combination to make the name of something you wear. They aren't the same letters.
oela

8. Add the correct math symbols to the equation below to make it true.

   2 ? 6 ? 4 ? 2 = 8

9. You are given 2 coins that add up to 30 cents. One is not a nickel. What are the coins?

10. You are a bus driver. At the first stop 12 people get on. At the second stop, 5 get off and 6 get on. At the third stop, 4 get off and 7 get on. At the fourth stop, 11 get off and 3 get on. At the fifth stop, 7 get off and 4 get on. At the sixth stop, 5 get off and 1 gets on. What colour are the bus driver's eyes?

Scoring

Give yourself 1 point for each correct answer.

1. Three. When you pull the second sock out of the drawer, it will either be the same colour as the first (a pair) or different from the first. If the socks are different colours, the third sock will make a pair with one of the first two socks, no matter what colour it is.

2. It would take 58 minutes. Each jump and slip propels the cricket 1 cm. After 57 minutes, the cricket will be 57 cm high. The next jump would be 3 cm, high enough to take him over the top of the bank in the 58th minute.

3. Push the cork *into* the bottle, then remove the coin.

4. A towel (or sponge).

5. Fire.

6. HO. To spell "horseshoe."

7. Add the letters SH to the front and CE to the end to form the word "Shoelace."

CONFIDENTIAL

8. You need x, +, ÷ [2 x 6 = 12 + 4 = 16 ÷ 2 = 8].

9. A quarter and a nickel. One of the coins is not a nickel — the other one is.

10. The same as yours — you are the bus driver!

How you rate . . .

0–3 Thank You for Your Application. You are on the wait-list for entry to the spy academy.

4–6 Success! You have been admitted to spy kindergarten.

7–8 A+. You have been awarded a scholarship for entry to Hawaiian spy school — bring your sunscreen and bathing suit for your advanced program in espionage and surfing.

9–10 Go to the Head of the Class. You will be teaching it, after all.

CONFIDENTIAL

DERRING-DO OR DERRING-DON'T?

Spies, especially agents in the field, need to be daring. How daring are you? Find out by choosing your best answer from each alternative below.

1. To complete a mission, would you rather . . .

   a. swim 50 m in water that *may* contain sharks, or . . .

   b. wade 2 m across a river that *absolutely* contains piranhas?

2. Would you rather . . .

   a. ski off a 10-storey-high ski jump, or . . .

   b. dive off a 10-m cliff into freezing cold water?

3. Would you rather . . .

   a. tell the truth about something, knowing you will be mildly punished, or . . .

   b. lie about it and either escape scot-free, or get a huge punishment if you're caught?

4. Would you rather . . .

   a. swing on a rope across a mountain gorge, or . . .

   b. ride a unicycle across a swaying bridge over that same gorge?

5. Would you rather . . .

   a. wrestle with 100 snakes, or . . .

   b. wrestle with 1 huge 100% deadly viper?

6. Would you rather . . .

   a. be trapped in a deep, dank, dark dungeon, or . . .

   b. be held hostage in a broiling hot shack in the desert?

7. Would you rather . . .

   a. be cornered by 6 enemy agents with swords, or . . .

   b. attend a bridge party with your grandma and her 18 best friends?

CONFIDENTIAL

8. Would you rather . . .
   a. eat a fish eyeball, or . . .
   b. eat a cow's liver, raw?

9. Would you rather . . .
   a. arm wrestle a giant octopus, or . . .
   b. stare down a polar bear?

10. Would you rather . . .
    a. land a plane, although you're not a pilot, or . . .
    b. race a motorcycle across a 1000-m-wide field that will be bombed into smithereens in 11.2 seconds?

Scoring

According to the I.M. Kiddin Espionage Research Agency, the ideal ratio of derring-do in a field agent is 89% daring and 11% caution. Add up your scores to see how your stats stack up.

1. a5 b10	6. a5 b10	
2. a10 b5	7. a15 b5	
3. a5 b10	8. a5 b10	
4. a5 b15	9. a10 b5	
5. a5 b10	10. a5 b10	

How you rate . . .

50–60 Sensible Sam. You are a smidge too cautious to make a good field agent, but that's okay — they tend to have very short lifespans. With your derring-do rate of 45%, you are perfectly suited to a nice analytical job back at headquarters — you get to send agents out into the field and hope they come back in one piece, while you are assured a long, healthy life.

65–75 Look-Before-You-Leap Leo. You are an almost even mixture of caution and bravado, with a derring-do rate of 59–68%. You are competent in the field, but when in doubt will err on the side of running home to mama. That's okay — she makes good cookies!

80–100 Leap-Before-You-Look Louie. You are the ideal sort of risk-taker needed to be a successful agent. With your derring-do rate of 72–90%, you tend to let intuition guide you, and your intuition almost always tells you to go for the bold move. However, you are not a bonehead — you won't take a dare when the odds of success are slim to nil.

105+ Leaping-Blindfolded-Hands-Tied Hans! You are off the charts, man! With a derring-do rate of 95%, you will do almost anything, no matter how crazy, or how low the odds are that you'll actually see tomorrow. You may wind up the ultimate hero, saving the day when all seems lost, but more likely, you'll just wind up bedridden with 42 broken bones and a really bad headache. Consider a career in UFC instead of espionage, for your own safety.

CONFIDENTIAL

WHERE IN THE WORLD?

What's the worst thing in the world? Getting lost on a mission to save it! To succeed as a spy, you need to know how to find your enemy, how to blend in when you're undercover in a foreign land and, most important, how to figure out where you are when you wake up and realize you've been captured! How spy-worthy are your geography skills? World-class or lost cause?

1. You receive an encrypted email from headquarters. You decipher it and find it's a clue to your next mission: *Meet contact: Big Ben.* From this you know you need to head to . . .
a. Ryogoku Kokugikan (Sumo Hall) in Tokyo.
b. Elizabeth Tower in London.
c. the closest NBA game.

2. You're on the trail of your arch-enemy Dr. Noyoudont. She's invented a chemical-filled bomb that could blow up a small nation. You've learned that the chemicals do not react well with oxygen. If she hopes to survive the launch, she must fire it from the highest altitude possible. You know she's terrified of flying, so where can you find her?
a. Mt. Everest.
b. The CN Tower in Toronto.
c. Burj Khalifa Tower in Dubai.

3. You've been sent to the Sleeper's Inn in Dawson, Yukon Territory. You get there, check into your room and find a car key and a message: *Take black SUV in hotel lot. You have three hours to drive to the US border and stop a rogue agent, in a red Ferrari, from crossing into Canada.* What do you do?
a. Panic! Three hours is impossible!
b. Panic! Even if I could make it to the border, how will I spot the agent?
c. Head out and stop the agent with no problem.

4. You've been drugged and kidnapped by enemy agents! When you come to, you manage to undo your bonds and jump out the window.

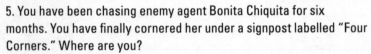

You find yourself surrounded by people on the run. Using your superior instinct for survival, you run, too. Before long, you notice a dozen crazed bulls hot on your heels! No wonder everyone is running! So here's the important question of the day: where are you?

a. Oxnard, California, home of the largest bovine population in America.

b. Pamplona, Spain — these runners *want* to be chased by bulls!

c. Chicago, Illinois, at a Chicago Bulls pre-game rally.

5. You have been chasing enemy agent Bonita Chiquita for six months. You have finally cornered her under a signpost labelled "Four Corners." Where are you?

a. Trafalgar Square, London.

b. The only place in the United States where four states meet.

c. At a famous restaurant in Sydney, Australia.

6. You have been paddling down a major river for days in search of your missing colleague, Agent X. Lax. You have passed many interesting sights along the way — ancient temples, crocodiles, hippos. Which river are you on?

a. The St. Lawrence.

b. The Amazon.

c. The Nile.

7. Your mission? To encourage Dmitri Valencovich, a Russian computer genius, to become a spy for your agency. After years of persuasion, he finally agrees to meet you, but only in the middle of a sea that borders his country and Turkey. You charter a very fancy Moldavian yacht (such extravagant fittings, all genuine tin!) and sail to:

a. the Red Sea.

b. the Black Sea.

c. the Sapphire Sea.

8. You are in pursuit of Nippy Weather, a mad scientist intent on turning the entire planet into a cube of ice! But where is his secret lair? You see a picture of him on Facebook, dressed in winter gear and surrounded by emperor penguins. Where should your agency direct their satellites to find him?

a. The Arctic Circle.

b. The San Francisco Zoo.

c. Antarctica.

9. You and your partner lose track of each other during a high-speed chase. You agreed that if you were separated, you would meet at the Colosseum. Where should you go?

a. The thirty-screen movie theatre down the street. You've been waiting to see the latest Bourne movie.

b. Rome.

c. Greece.

10. You're on the run! You must reach the safety of your embassy in Afghanistan. The embassy is in Afghanistan's capital, which is . . .

a. Tehran.

b. Baghdad.

c. Kabul.

Scoring

Give yourself 1 point for each right answer.

1. b — The bell, which has been commonly known as Big Ben, is within the clock tower.

2. a

3. c — The border with Alaska is just over 100 km away. There is only one road to get there. Good thing it's summer or it would be closed!

4. b — It's Pamplona's annual Running of the Bulls.

5. b

6. c

7. b

8. c

9. b

10. c

How you rate . . .

0 Lost Cause. Do you use a compass to get to school?

1–3 On Your Way. With a little help from a GPS and Google, you can get yourself on the right track.

4–7 Way to Go. You obviously pay attention to the world beyond your front door!

8–10 First Class. You are a walking atlas and fount of information!

CONFIDENTIAL

THE FINAL EXAM

You have now been thoroughly trained in Spyness. Are you 100% ready to join the forces of sneakiness? Perhaps, perhaps not. Before you can be given your diploma of duplicity, you must take — and pass! — this final exam. Ready, set, shhhhh!

Part I: Multiple Choice

1. You want a job working for MI6. In the interview, they ask you what MI6 stands for. What do you say?
a. "Mission Intelligence, Level 6."
b. "Directorate of Military Intelligence, Section 6."
c. "Am I six?"

2. Which of the people below was not a fellow spy?
a. Classical composer Wolfgang Amadeus Mozart.
b. Nineteen-forties film star Hedy Lamarr.
c. Sir Robert Baden-Powell, founder of the Boy Scouts.

3. You've decided you'd like to pursue a career in the science of scrambling and unscrambling messages. What is it called?
a. Cryptology
b. Stenography
c. Mesology

4. Your identity has been compromised. You need to get out of South Africa — fast. The police are watching the borders. What does headquarters send you?
a. A hot-air balloon.
b. A shoe.
c. A jet-pack.

5. Which of the following has nothing to do with secret codes?

a. An Enigma machine.

b. The Atbash code.

c. The code of conduct.

Part II: True or False

6. Ian Fleming, the creator of James Bond, based his character on actual spies he knew during World War II.

7. CIA stands for Central Intelligence Agency.

8. Counterspies look after a spy agency's money.

9. Homing pigeons have been used to carry secret messages.

10. A dead drop is a nickname for an agent who jumps from a plane into enemy territory.

11. The best spy is a person who appears average or dull.

12. Double agents work for two spy organizations at the same time.

13. Spies are sometimes hired by businesses to find out more about industry competitors.

14. Robotic bats and rats have been developed for use by spy agencies and the military.

15. Russia's spy agency is called RIA.

16. A real spy training camp called Camp X was once located in Halifax.

17. A real spy training camp for dogs was once located in Britain.

18. Spies need to be physically fit.

19. The CIA once tried to train a cat as a spy. On its first mission, the cat was run over by a taxi and it died.

20. The CIA maintains a website just for kids.

Part III: Extra Credit

21. You have been chasing your enemy, Pus Eye, across Asia. You have finally caught up to her on a remote island. Alas, she's dead! Her body is lying in a clearing in the middle of the island. You are both wearing packs. Hers is closed. Yours is open. What is in her pack?

22. You have been assigned to make contact with a sleeper agent and activate him. He lives alone in a small cottage. He does not like to go out much, so he has everything he needs delivered to his cottage. Dressed as a courier, you arrive at the cottage on Thursday morning. You notice the front door is partly open. You peek inside and you see the sleeper agent is lying on the living room floor — dead! You look around for clues. On the porch you see there are two bottles of warm milk, Monday's newspaper, a catalogue, flyers and several pieces of unopened mail. You realize his assassin was one of the delivery people. Who put your sleeper agent to sleep — permanently?

23. You are in charge of hiring a new recruit. Several applicants come to the office. Your assistant gives each applicant a sealed envelope and says, "Please report to the interview room on the fifth floor." As soon as he is alone, one of the applicants opens the envelope and reads the contents. Then he goes directly to the third floor. What do you do, and why?

24. In retaliation for foiling her bombing attempt, Dr. Noyoudont had you secretly drugged and kidnapped. You wake up in a strange room. There are four walls, and each has a window that faces south. A bear walks by. What colour is the bear, and how does this help you figure out where you're being held captive?

25. You believe a colleague in your organization is really a mole. You report your suspicions to headquarters and receive a coded letter back with their reply:

12345678
1234 is an atmospheric condition (rhymes with fist).
34567 supports a plant.
4567 is to grab or make off with.
678 is a name.

Is your colleague a mole or not?

CONFIDENTIAL

Scoring

Give yourself 1 point for each correct answer for Part I.
Give yourself 1 point for each correct answer for Part II.
Give yourself 10 points for each correct answer for Part III.

Part I

1. b
2. a
3. a
4. b — it's a false passport.
5. c
6. T
7. T
8. F
9. T
10. F
11. T
12. T
13. T
14. T
15. F
16. F
17. T
18. T
19. T
20. T
21. Her parachute.

22. The newspaper delivery person, otherwise the paper would have continued to be delivered after Monday.

23. Hire him. The letter inside the sealed envelope said, "You are our kind of person. Come directly to my office on the third floor for your job offer."

24. The bear is white. You are in the North Pole!

25. No. The message, decoded, reads, "Mistaken." [Mist, stake, take, Ken].

How you rate . . .

0–1 Fail. You are definitely sneaky — you clearly skipped to the end of the book without reading any of the other quizzes! Go back and try again from the beginning!

2–10 Borderline. You have made it into NME spy agency by the skin of your teeth! Your first mission? To remove the skin from your teeth.

11–25 Acceptable. You have achieved a passing grade in your final exam. As a result, you will be passing the salt — your first mission is to work undercover in a salt mine! Make sure to get to know the dwarf named Grumpy — he is your contact. You will soon learn why working in a salt mine helped give him this code name.

CONFIDENTIAL

26–45 Solid B! You are destined for Great Things! Unfortunately, your destination was supposed to be Langley, Virginia, not Great Things, Manitoba. Never fear, with your superior spy skills you will figure out how to get from Manitoba to Virginia in time for your first mission — teaching map reading to new spy-school students.

46–59 Head of the Class! Your score is so high you are being assigned to in-the-field duty immediately. Your mission: to find people who cheated on their final exam. Then neutralize them.

60–70 Mission Accomplished! You clearly are not a newbie spy, but rather a supremely talented and vastly experienced agent. This was your exit exam from the gruelling life of espionage. Your license to kill is revoked and you may now return to civilian life. But don't worry — you won't be bored. The staggering fortune you have amassed during your successful spy career has been piling up in a Swiss bank account, just waiting for you to input your activation code and access it. Congratulations, and enjoy your life of leisure and luxury!

Look for these other great quiz books!

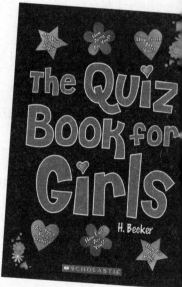